Connect the Dots

Book for Kids

Challenging and Fun Dot to Dot Puzzles

DP Kids

©2017

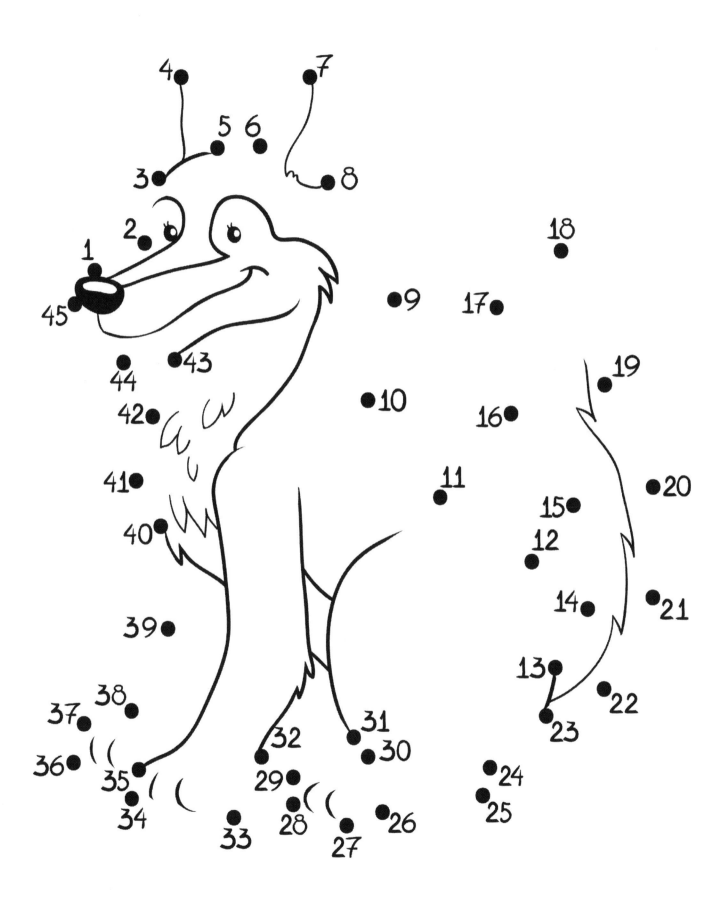

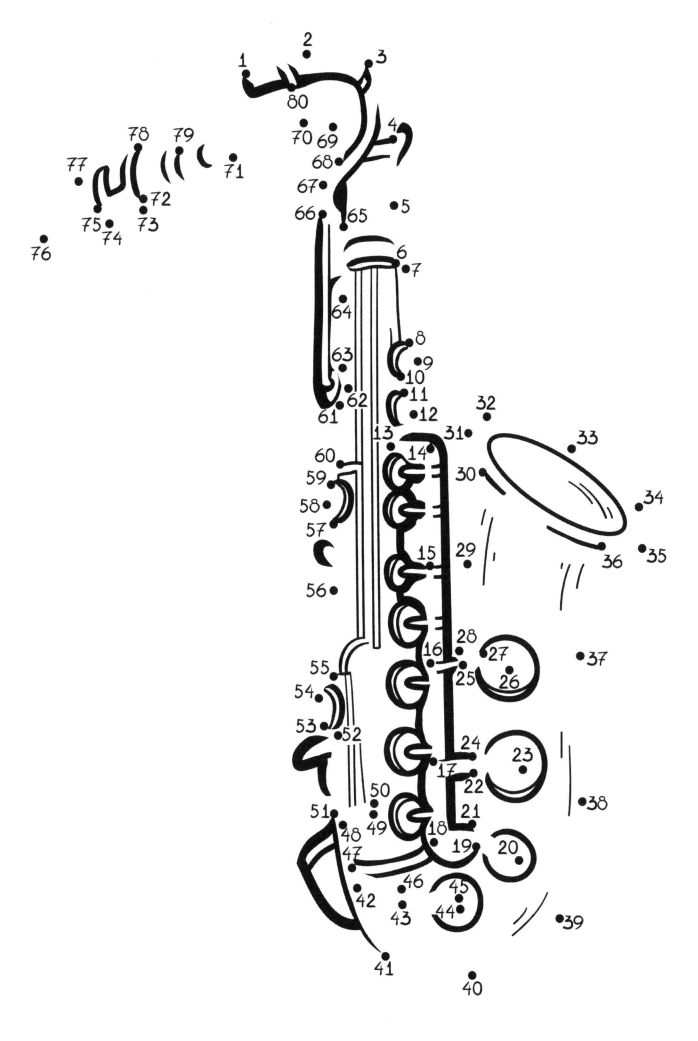

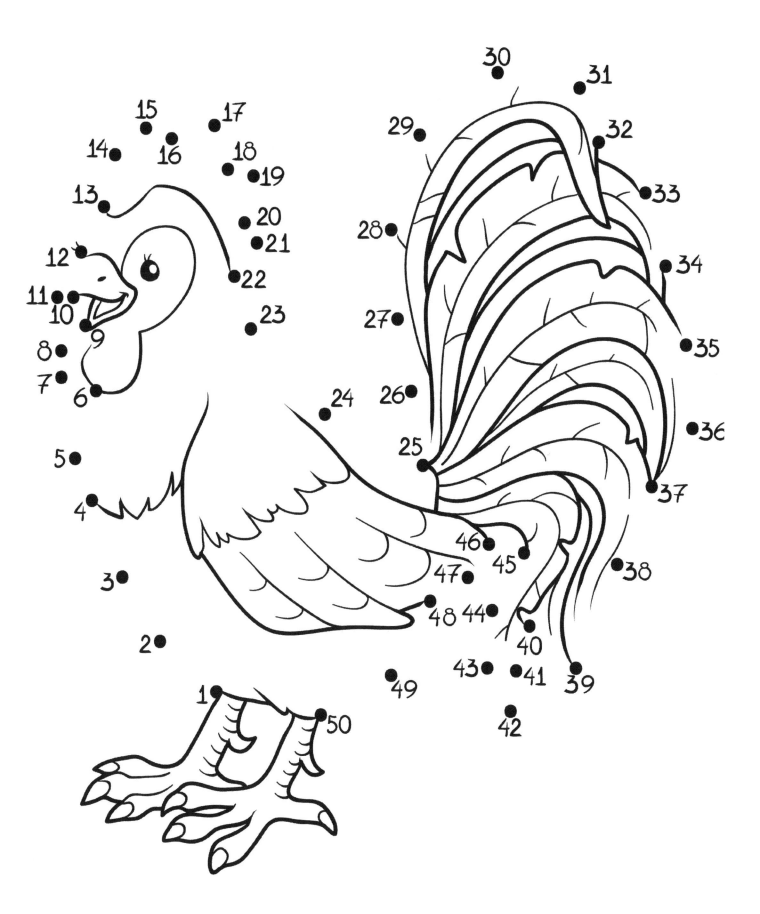

When you come to an asterisk * in the puzzle this indicates that the current line ends. Look for the next numberin a different part of the puzzle and draw a new line starting there.

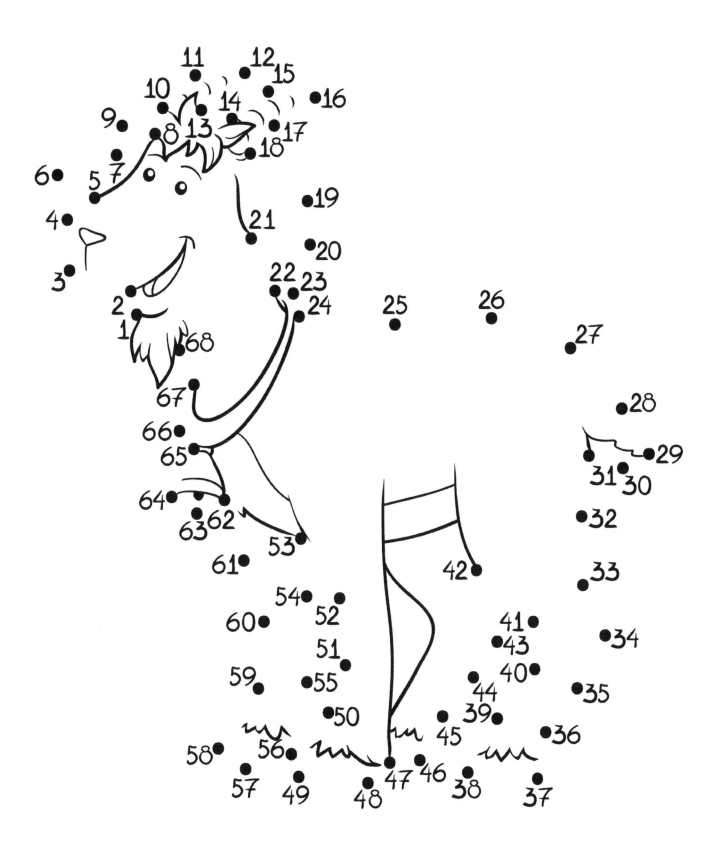

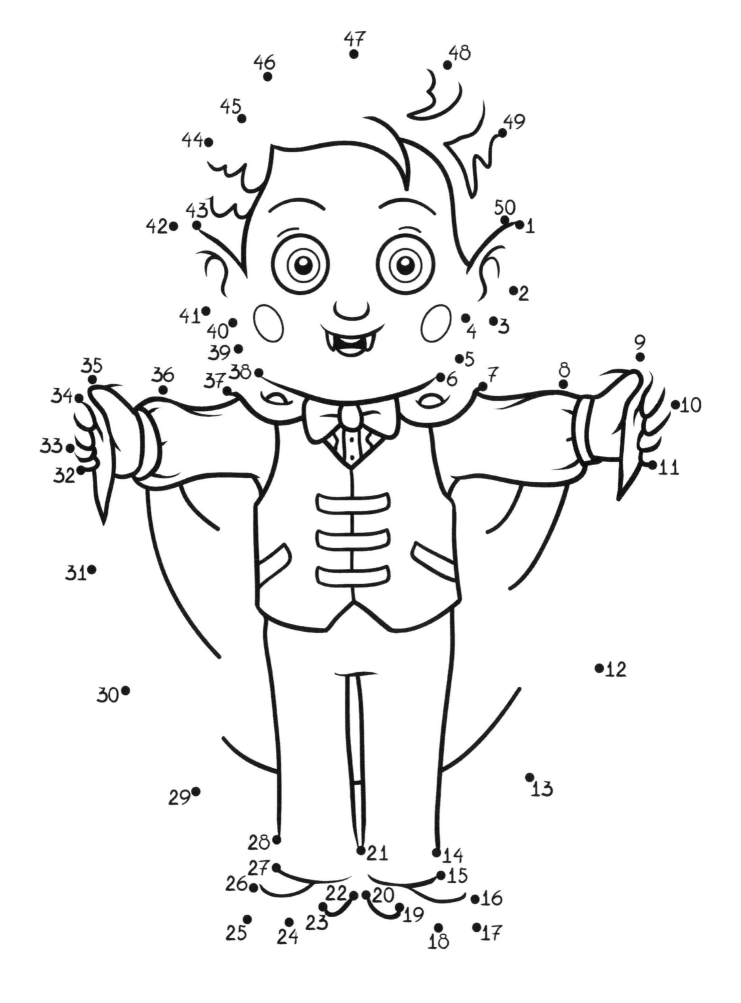

When you come to an asterisk * in the puzzle this indicates that the current line ends. Look for the next numberin a different part of the puzzle and draw a new line starting there.

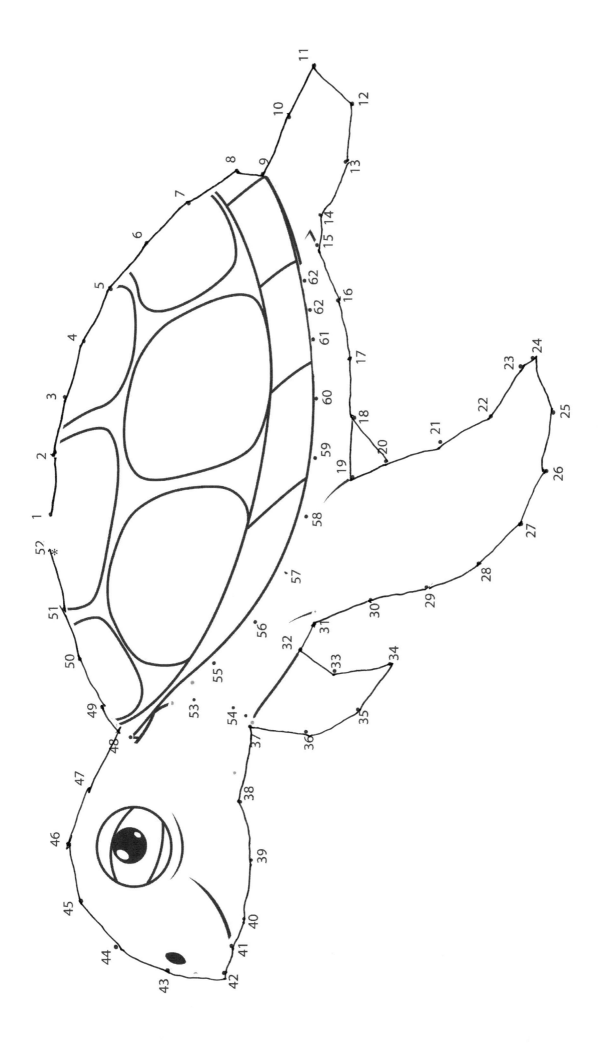

When you come to an asterisk * in the puzzle this indicates that the current line ends. Look for the next number in a different part of the puzzle and draw a new line starting there.

When you come to an asterisk * in the puzzle this indicates that the current line ends. Look for the next number in a different part of the puzzle and draw a new line starting there.

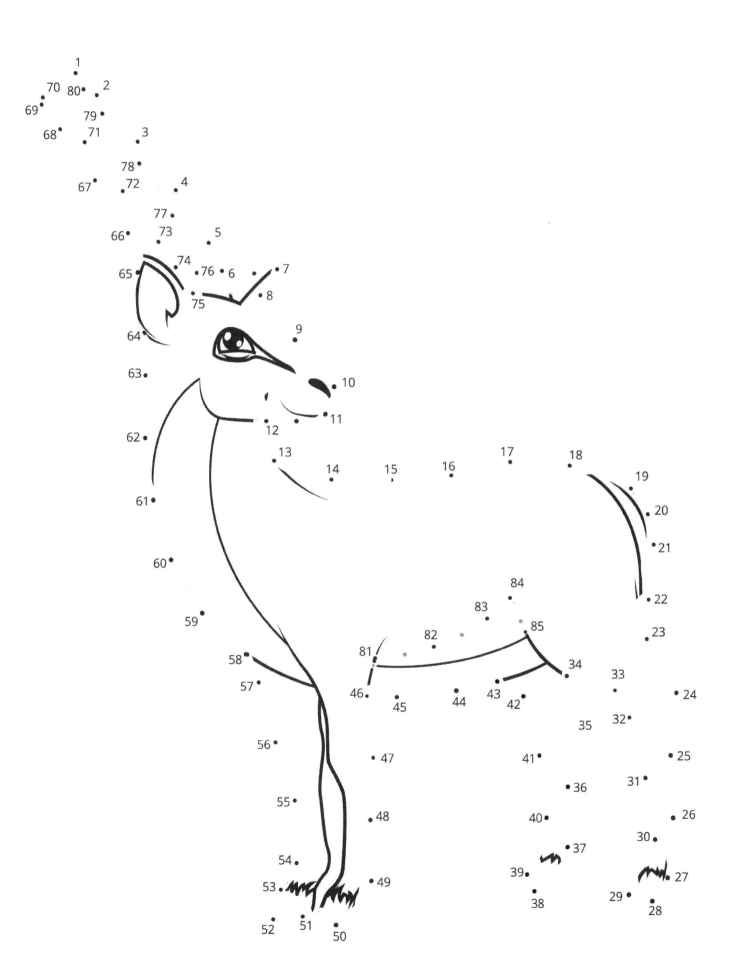

When you come to an asterisk * in the puzzle this indicates that the current line ends. Look for the next number in a different part of the puzzle and draw a new line starting there.

When you come to an asterisk * in the puzzle this indicates that the current line ends. Look for the next number in a different part of the puzzle and draw a new line starting there.

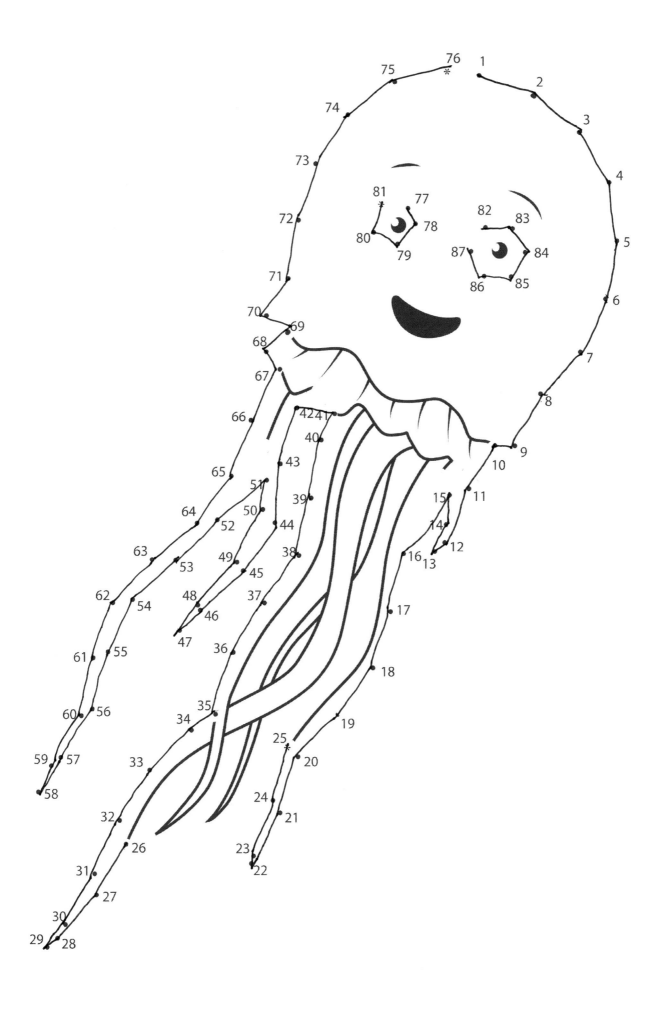

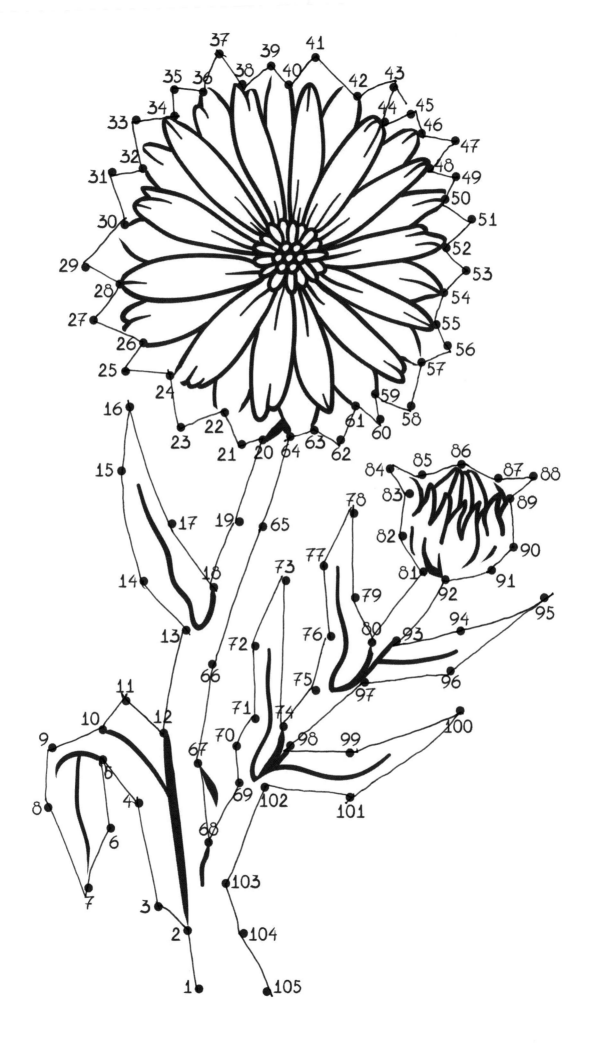

When you come to an asterisk * in the puzzle this indicates that the current line ends. Look for the next number in a different part of the puzzle and draw a new line starting there.

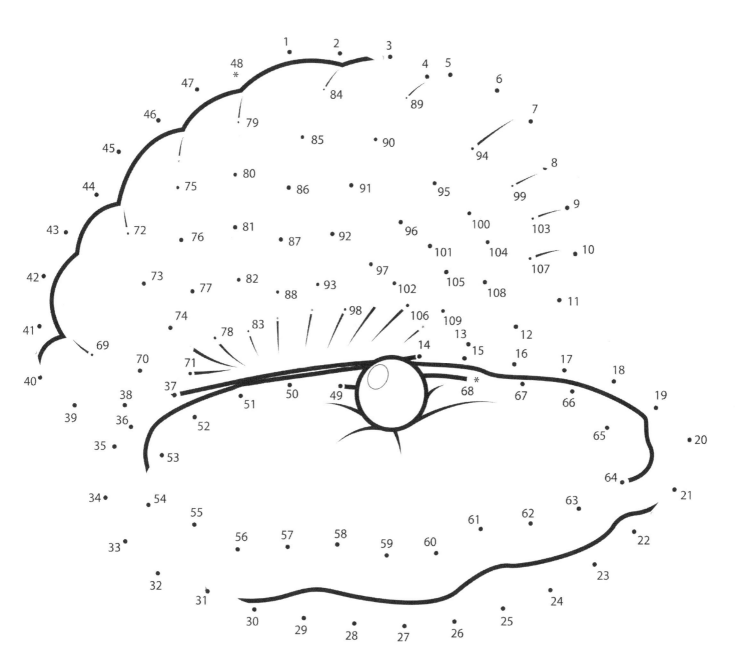

When you come to an asterisk * in the puzzle this indicates that the current line ends. Look for the next number in a different part of the puzzle and draw a new line starting there.

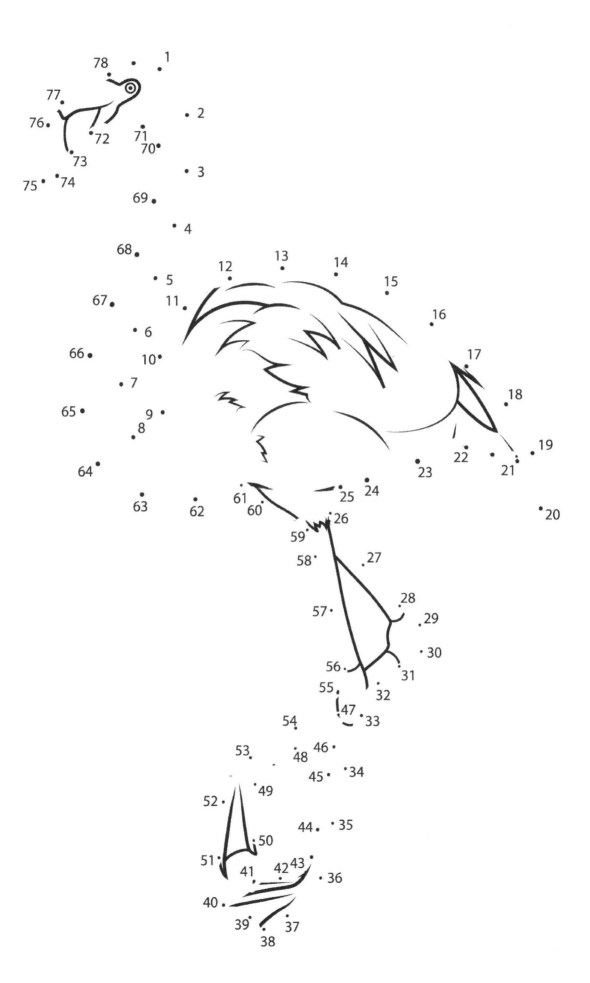

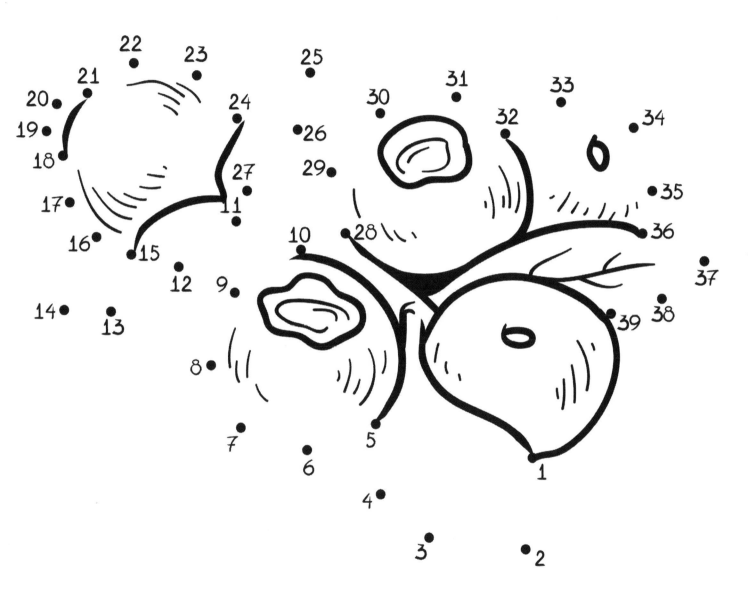

When you come to an asterisk * in the puzzle this indicates that the current line ends. Look for the next number in a different part of the puzzle and draw a new line starting there.

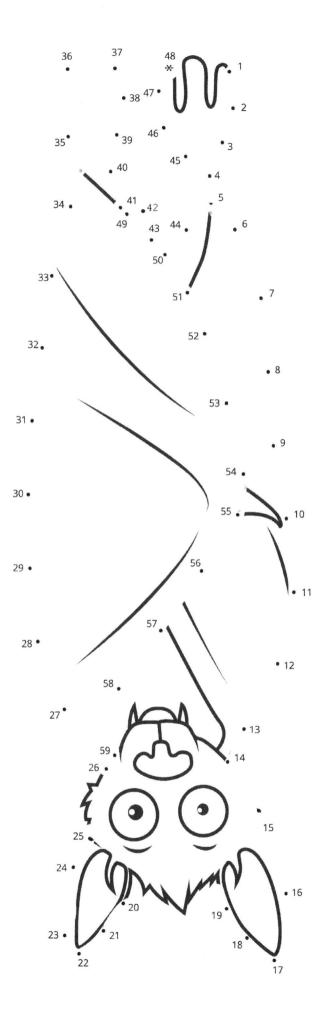

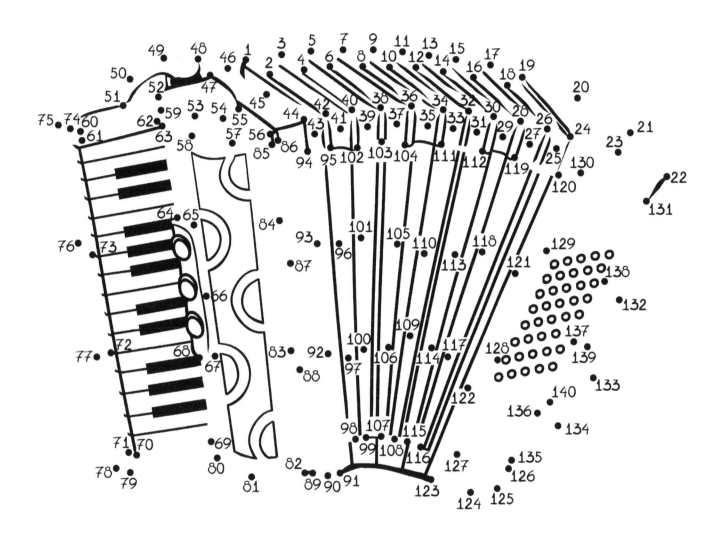

When you come to an asterisk * in the puzzle this indicates that the current line ends. Look for the next numberin a different part of the puzzle and draw a new line starting there.

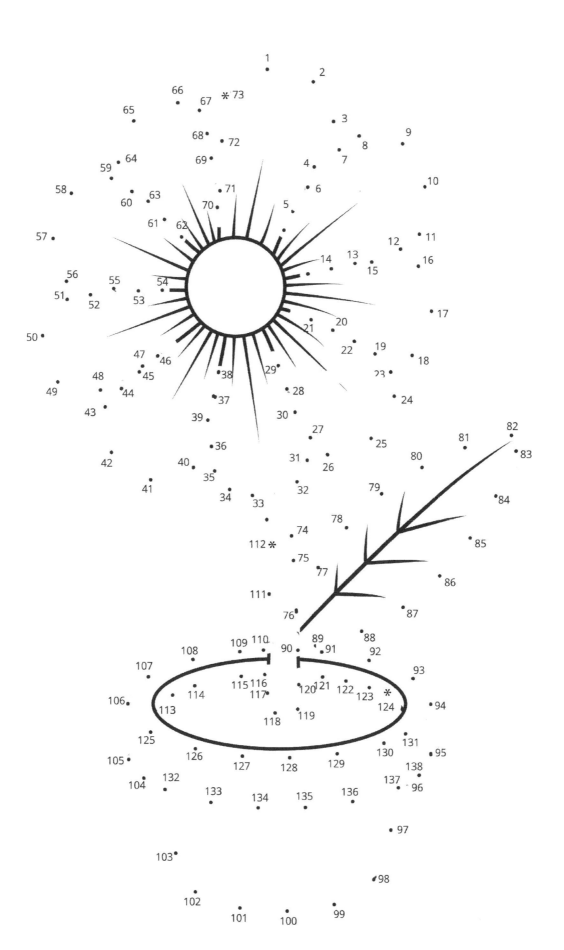

When you come to an asterisk * in the puzzle this indicates that the current line ends. Look for the next number in a different part of the puzzle and draw a new line starting there.

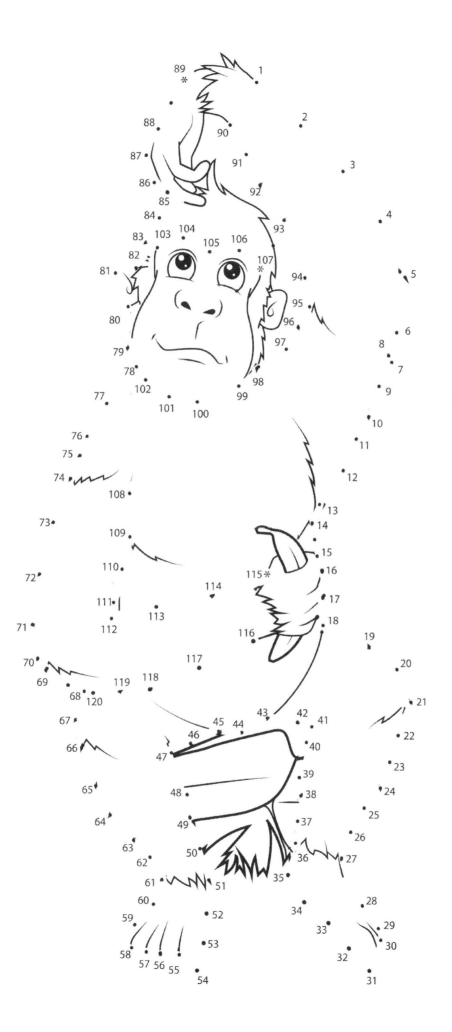

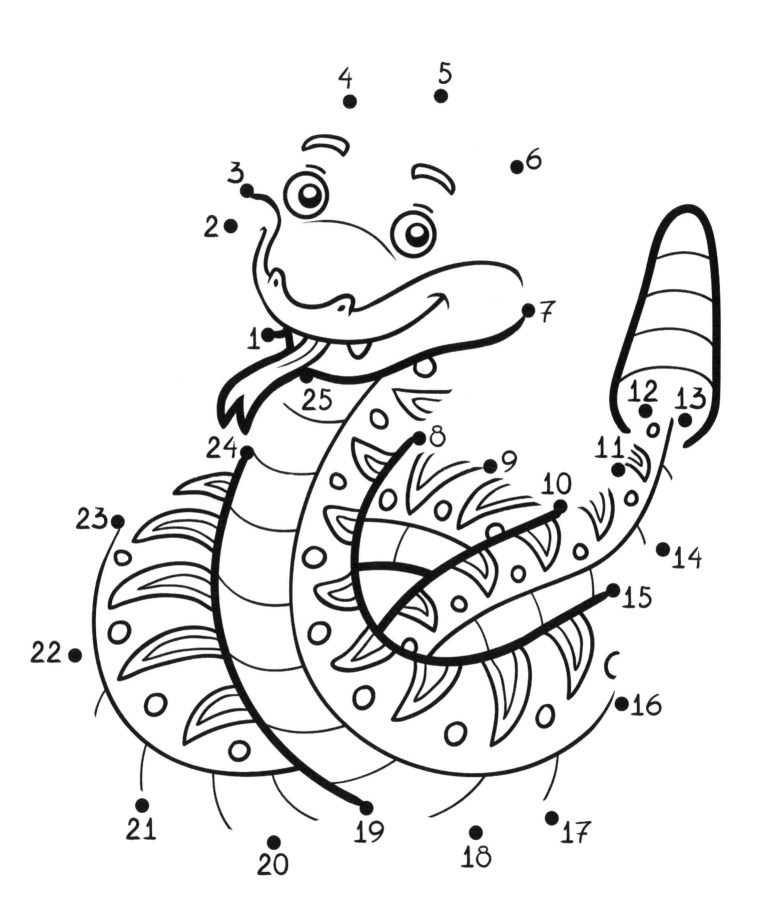

When you come to an asterisk * in the puzzle this indicates that the current line ends. Look for the next number in a different part of the puzzle and draw a new line starting there.

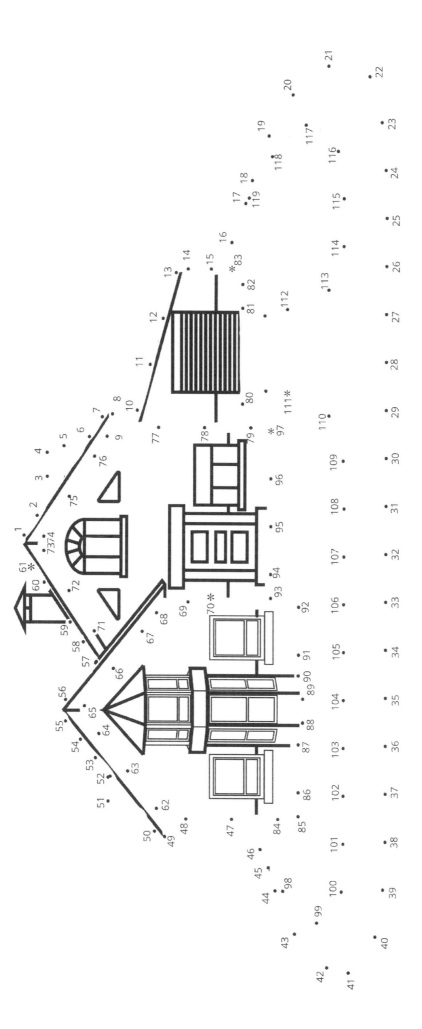

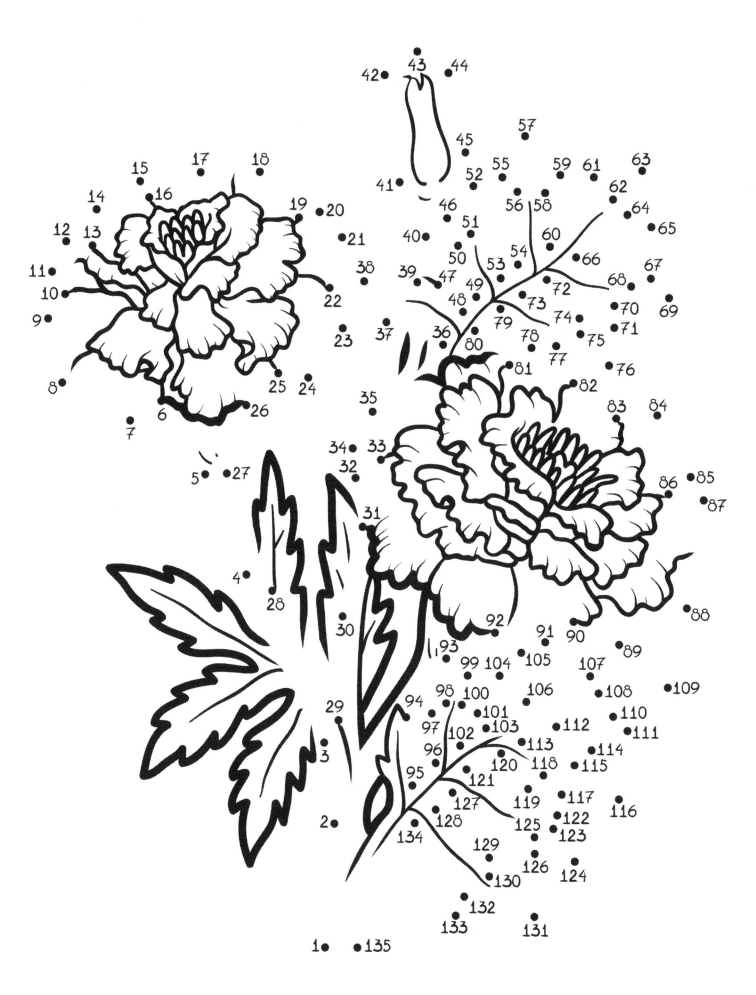

When you come to an asterisk * in the puzzle this indicates that the current line ends. Look for the next number in a different part of the puzzle and draw a new line starting there.

When you come to an asterisk * in the puzzle this indicates that the current line ends. Look for the next number in a different part of the puzzle and draw a new line starting there.

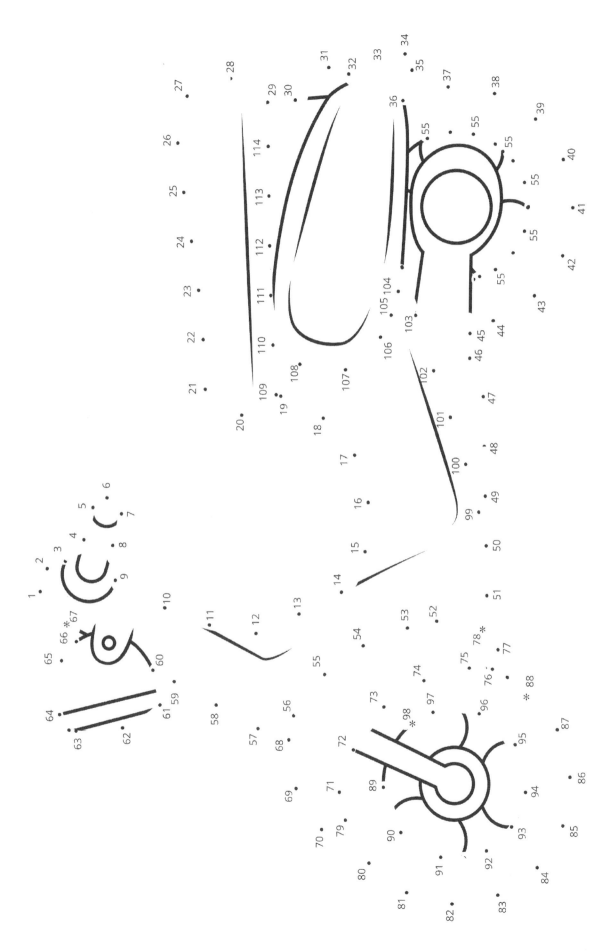

When you come to an asterisk * in the puzzle this indicates that the current line ends. Look for the next numberin a different part of the puzzle and draw a new line starting there.

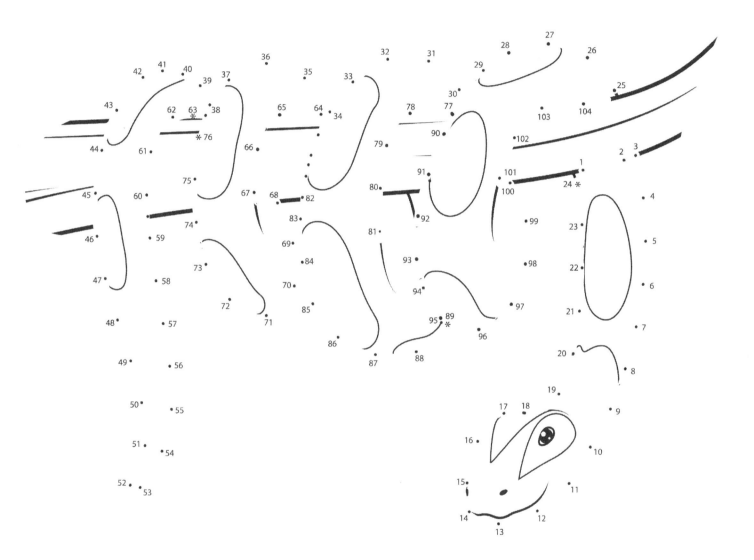

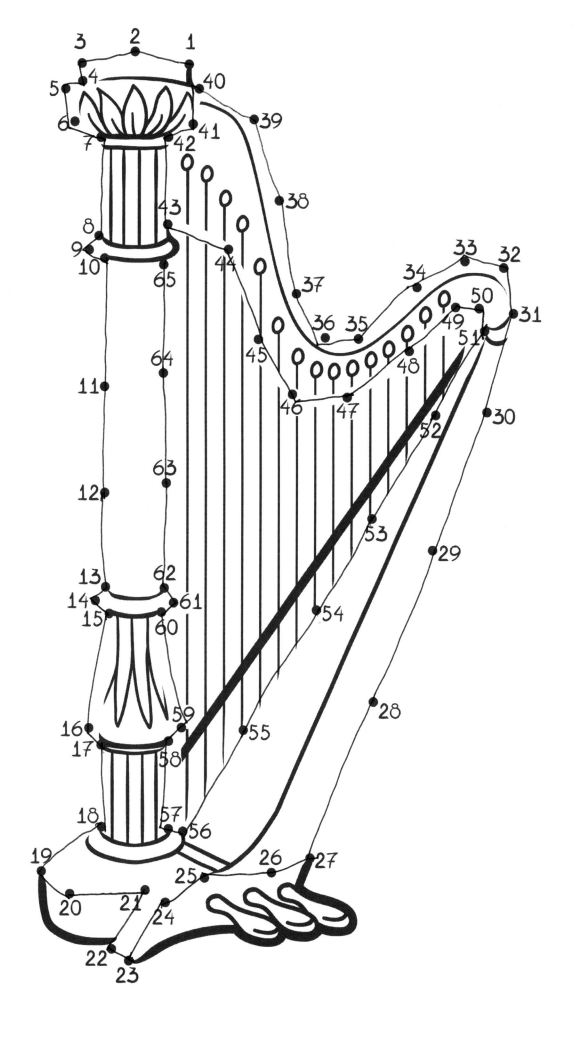

When you come to an asterisk * in the puzzle this indicates that the current line ends. Look for the next numberin a different part of the puzzle and draw a new line starting there.

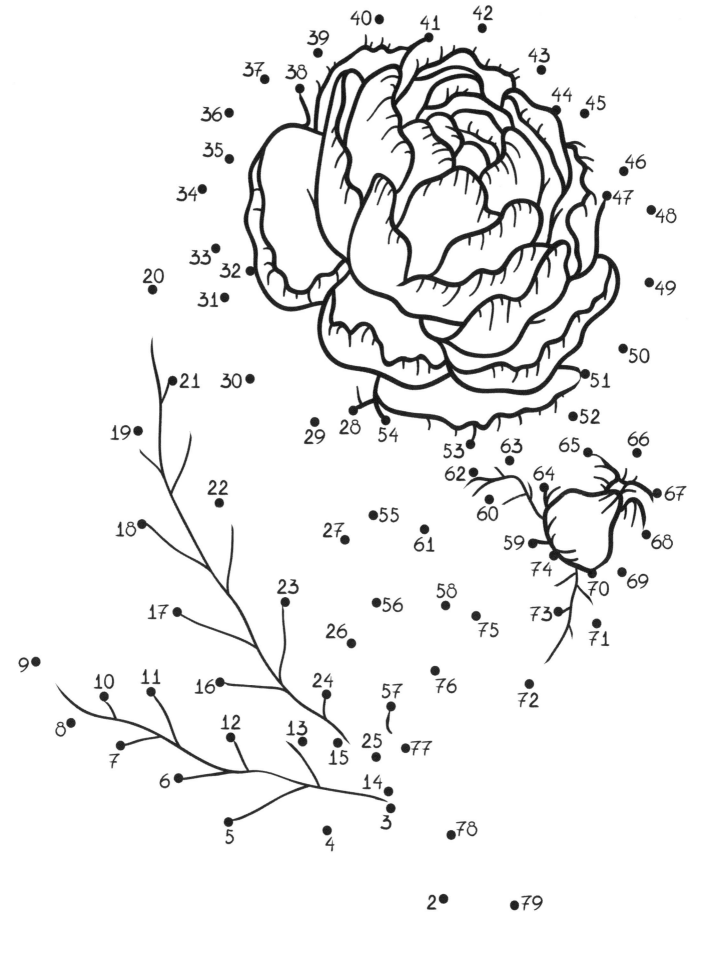

When you come to an asterisk * in the puzzle this indicates that the current line ends. Look for the next number in a different part of the puzzle and draw a new line starting there.

When you come to an asterisk * in the puzzle this indicates that the current line ends. Look for the next number in a different part of the puzzle and draw a new line starting there.

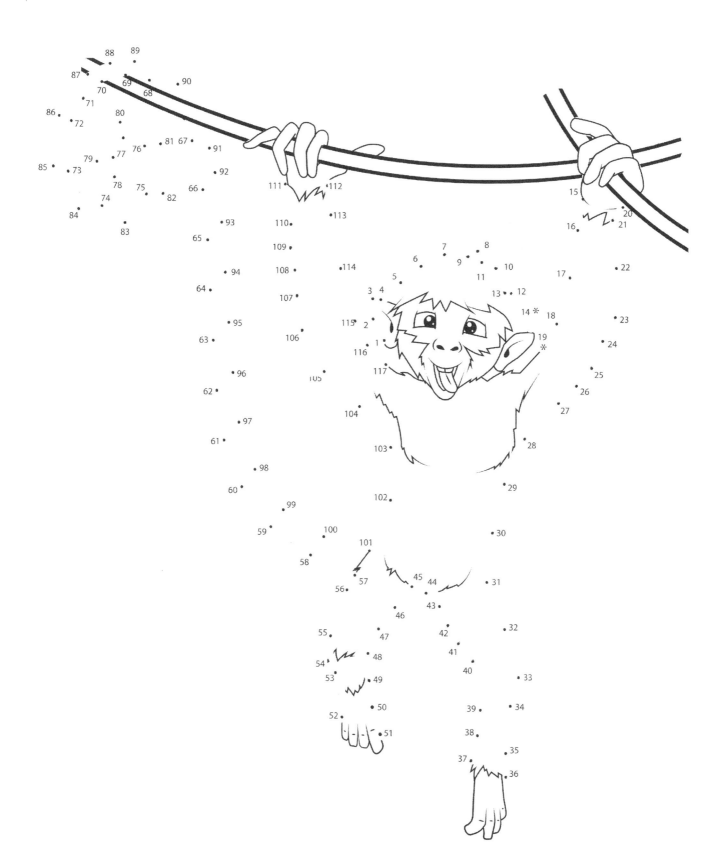

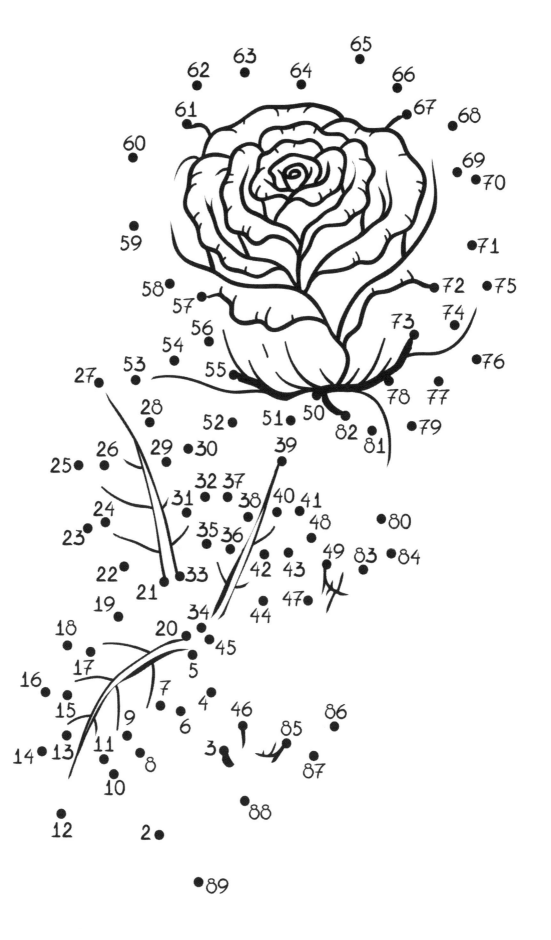

When you come to an asterisk * in the puzzle this indicates that the current line ends. Look for the next number in a different part of the puzzle and draw a new line starting there.

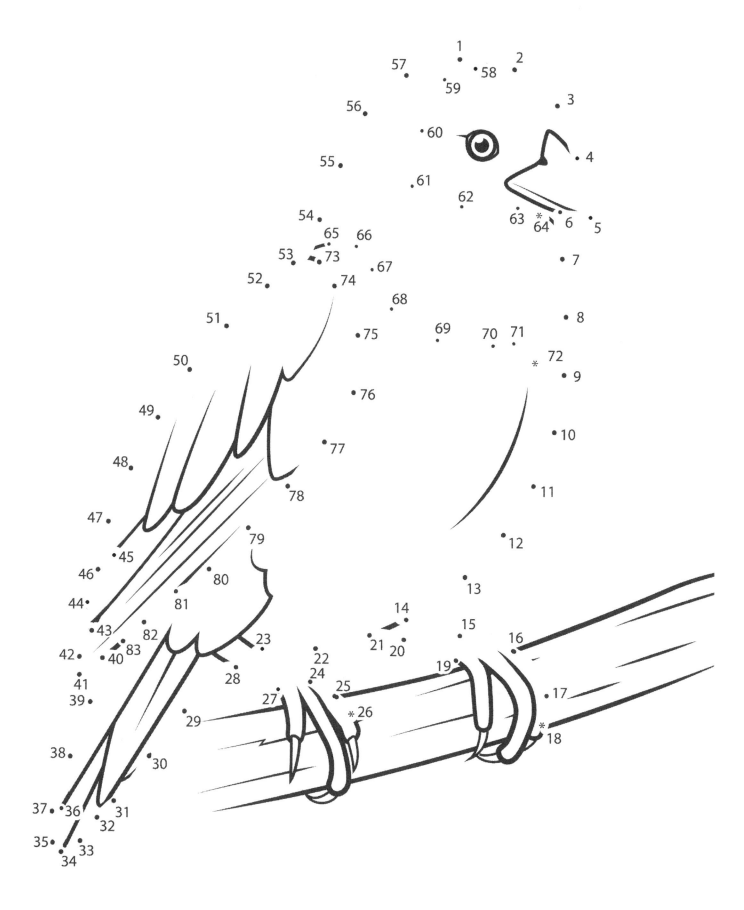

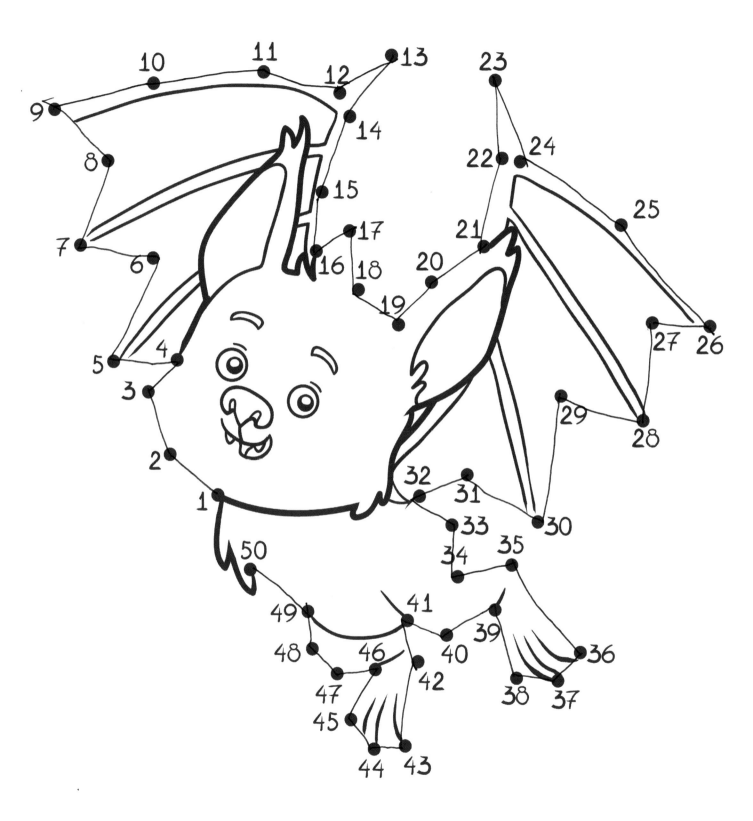

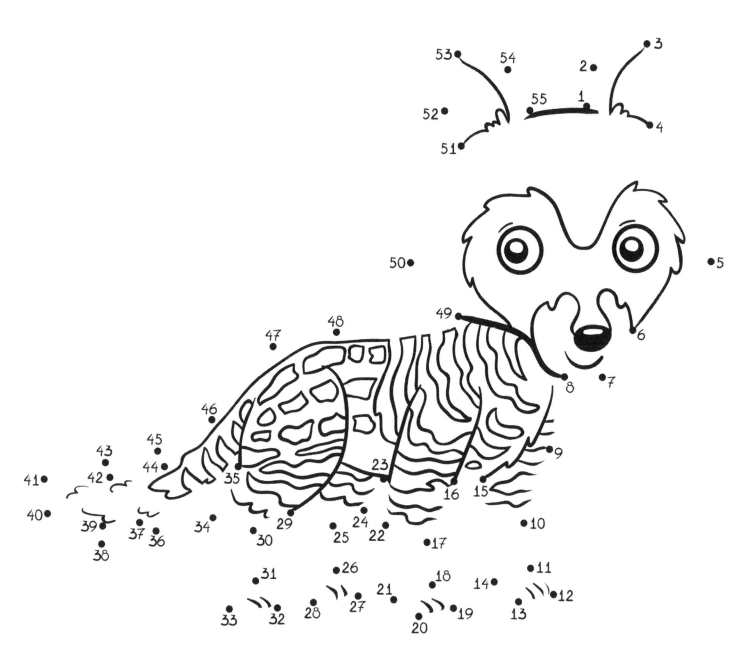

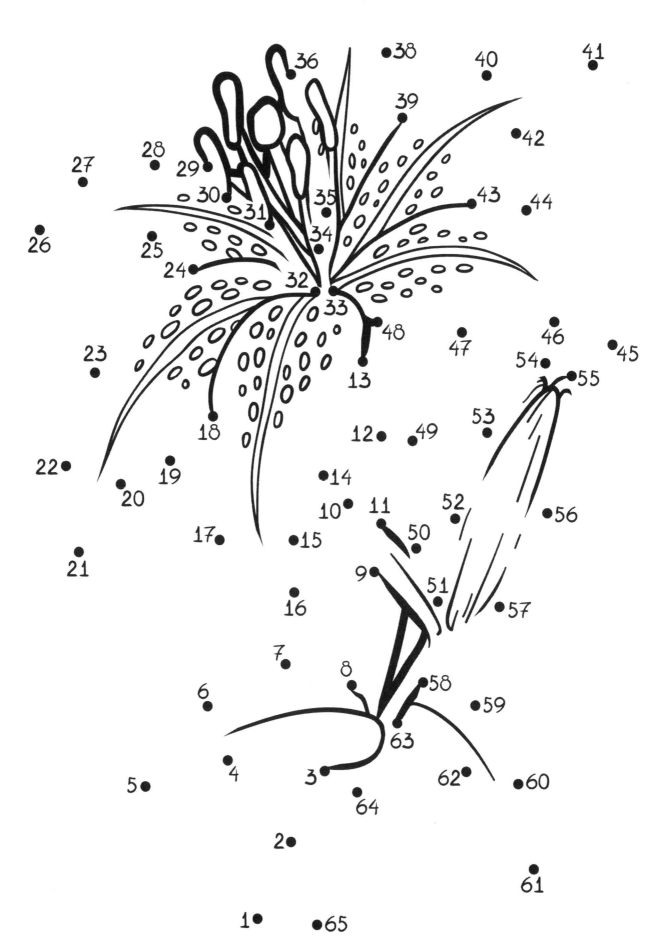

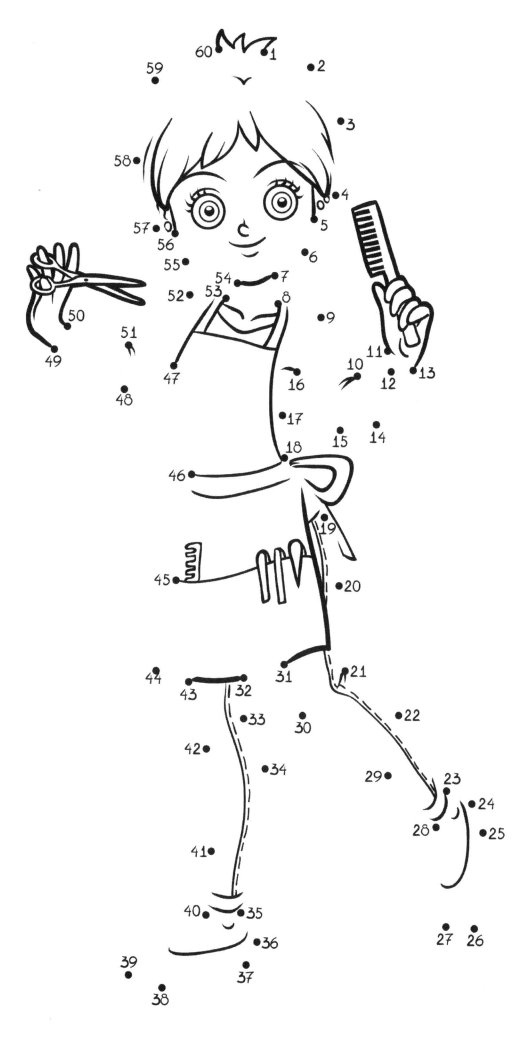

Made in the USA
San Bernardino, CA
22 September 2018